I can help!

Written and Illustrated by
Jessica Smith

Published by
Carpe Diem Publishers
P.O. Box 2146
San Benito, TX 78586
806-433-6321

www.carpediempublishers.com
I Can Help!

Printed in the United States of America
ISBN: 978-1-949215-11-3

To my very sweet children-

All three of you help me in more ways than you know! Your helpfulness has not gone un-noticed! I love you Nathan, Nelle and Callum!

Love, Mom

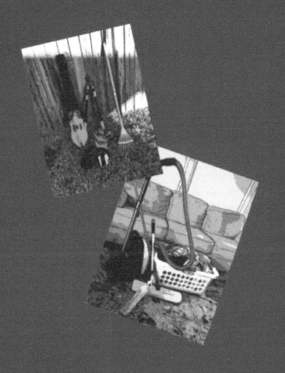

I can help clean the FLOORS.

I can help great-grandpa roast the S'MORES.

I can help dad with the VENTILATION.

I can help plan our VACATION.

I can help with the RAKE.

I can help prime the STEAKS.

I can help take out the TRASH.

I can help baby with his RASH.

I can help mom with the DISHES.

I can help great-grandma feed the FISHES.

I can help teach our dogs to read a BOOK.

I can help teach sister how to COOK.

I can help keep watch for BUGS.

I can help beat out the RUGS.

I can help great-grandpa change the OIL.

I can help grandma seed the SOIL.

I can help dust the BLINDS.

I can help the peculiar MINDS.

I can help cousin curb her EYEBROWS.

I can help grandpa with his big COWS.

I can help myself count the SHEEP.

I can help myself fall ASLEEP.

CPSIA information can be obtained
at www.ICGtesting.com
Printed in the USA
BVHW022032060821
613822BV00006B/474